Zoé de Las Cases

SECRET NEW YORK

Colouring for mindfulness

hamlyn

An Hachette UK Company
www.hachette.co.uk

First published in France in 2015 by Éditions Marabout

This edition published in Great Britain in 2015 by Hamlyn,
a division of Octopus Publishing Group Ltd
Carmelite House
50 Victoria Embankment
London EC4Y 0DZ
www.octopusbooks.co.uk

ISBN 978-0-600-63365-5

A CIP catalogue record for this book is available from the British Library.

Printed and bound in Italy

10 9 8 7 6 5 4 3 2 1

Layout: aliocha MULTIMÉDIA
Acknowledgements: Théodora Méneur
Senior Production Manager: Katherine Hockley

THIS BOOK BELONGS TO:

....

Come In
WE'RE
OPEN

WELCOME
TO MY SECRET NEW YORK!

New York – the city of dreams…Elegant, energetic, dynamic, magical, breathtaking… A city for the creative and ambitious, and a destination where there is always something new to discover.

Enjoy walking along the imposing avenues and breathing in the unique atmosphere of Brooklyn. After a walk along the High Line, admire the Statue of Liberty from the Staten Island ferry and lose yourself among the giant screens and neon lights of Times Square. Pick up a ticket for a Broadway show and rediscover your childhood at Luna Park on Coney Island. Taste Italian specialities in Little Italy, try out the city's burgers, discover the lively, bustling atmosphere of Chelsea Market and, as night falls, mix with the crowds in the West Village.

Get rid of your stress and decorate the most cosmopolitan city in the world with a thousand colours. Discover your hidden artist and, after a few pencil strokes, forget your everyday worries and tap into the 24-hour energy of the Big Apple.

DÉTOX
BIO
AB

NEW YORK
CAFFE
BIOLOGICO
COFFEE
FROM ORGANIC AGRICULTURE

PUKCO
chamomile & vanilla
ORGANIC HERBAL
TEA

ARGAN
Oil
ARGAN
Oil

OLIVIA

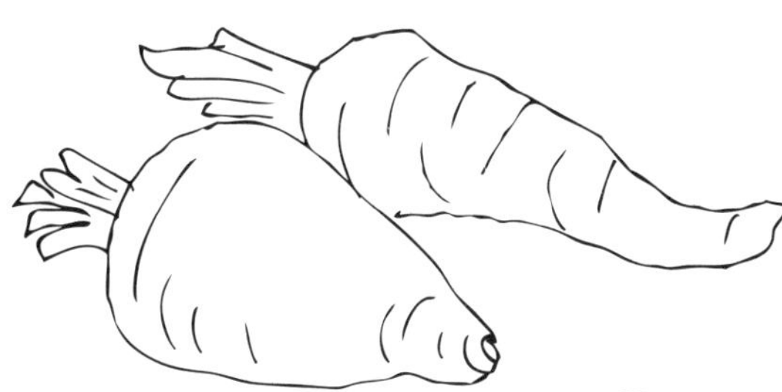

Puressentiel
BOIS DE ROSE
D'ASIE
1
ORGANIC OIL
PURE & NATURAL
Puressentiel
1

Clearspring
ORGANIC
TOFU
FIRM & SILKEN
LOW FAT
DAIRY FREE
GLUTEN FREE

PRIMÉAL
Graines de
lin doré
AB
250g

ADULT / ADULTE
NATURAL
1
LARGE BREED

NATURAL

AUDIO 2
SONY
STEREO
WALKMAN
A
D-C60
TDK
IN
OUT
MENU
iPod
Playlists
Artists
Songs
Contacts
Settings
menu
MENU
ONE
ONE
INTERNAL BLOMBRUSH
LOST TONGUES
CLOSED VESSEL

N°3 683

42ND
STREET

Delicious Desserts
Cakes
Pies
Pastry
CHOCOLATE PECAN
SALADS
57
HEINZ

FISH MARKET
411
Public
FISH MARKET
THE OLDEST FISH MA RET IN NEW-YORK

CHELSEA
FLOWER
MARKET

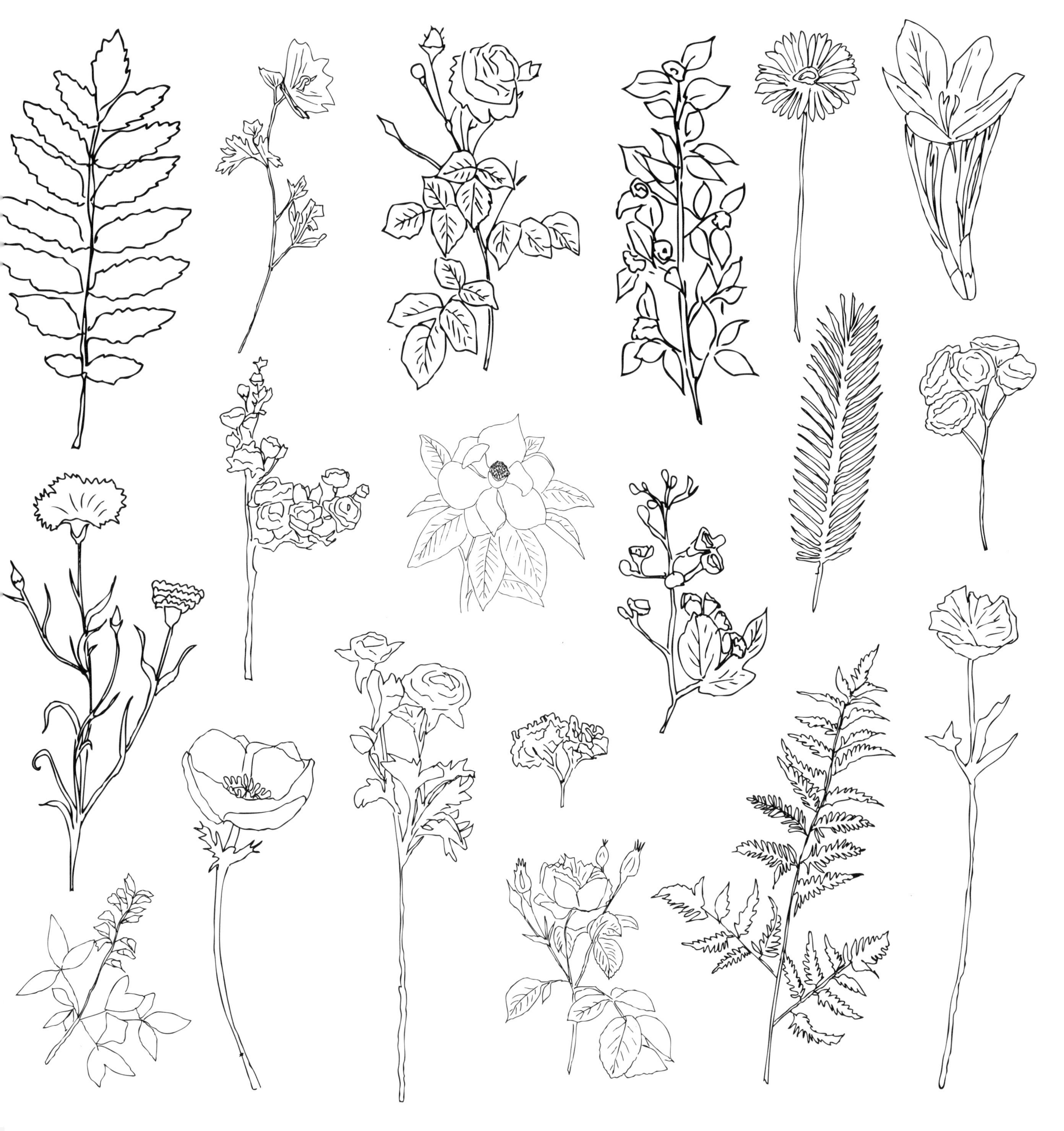

WE FIGHT BAC
PALACE
WEST SIDE STORY
TICKETMASTER.COM 212-307-4100
BROADWAY'S
SURE
THING
CHICAGO
ongs to...
WEST SIDE STORY
FUEL
OPEN
TIMES SQUARE
INFORMATION

ICE CREAM
CENTRAL PARK
Central Park
MENU

Central Park Lower Loop

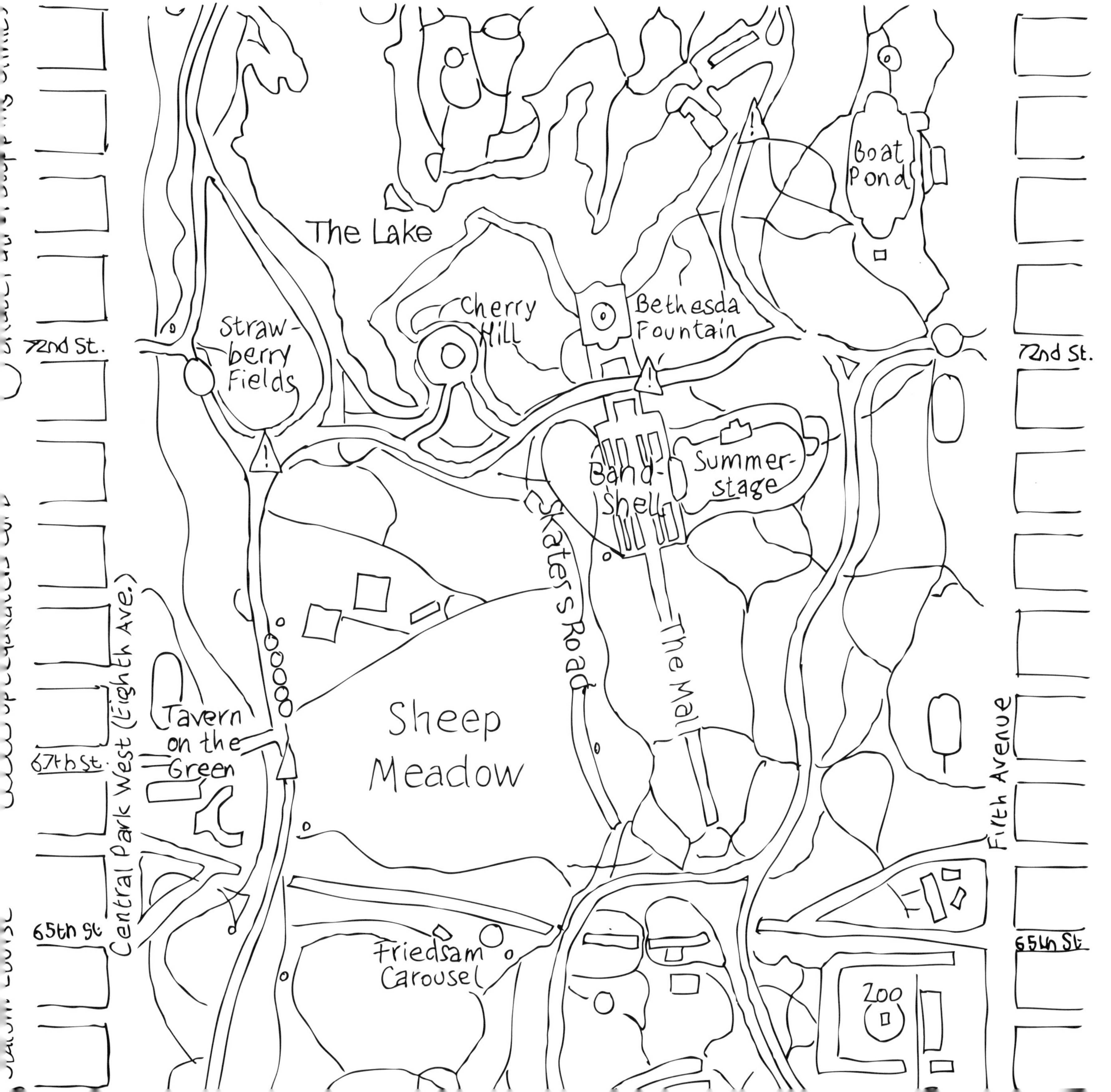

The Lake

Boat Pond

Cherry Hill

Bethesda Fountain

Straw-berry Fields

72nd St.

72nd St.

Band-Shell

Summer-stage

Skaters Road

The Mall

Sheep Meadow

Tavern on the Green

67th St.

Central Park West (Eighth Ave.)

Fifth Avenue

65th St.

65th St.

Friedsam Carousel

Zoo

CONEY ISLAND
SOUVENIR S
& GIFT SHOP
BATTERIES
T-SHIRTS
SANDALS
FILM • SUNTAN OIL • SUNGLASSES • BEACH TOWELS
ICE CREAM
RUBY'S
ICE CREAM
FRIES
COLD BEER

SANTA CLAUS
JAN 8 1981
USA
POP
POP
POW
Cola Coca

Modern
SNACK
BAR
SAUERBRATEN
SS CRABS
BEER & WINE
COCKTAILS

LI & SONS
285
LI & SONS · 285
RKI
LI & SONS
YOUR FOOD
AY SUGGESTIONS
DUCK • GEESE
WILD TUR •
PIGS •
AVAILABLE

TH AVENUE
BUILDING
MoMa
EXPOSITION

NEW YORK

New York

NEW YORK

NEW YORK

FREE
FREE
THE 313 WRITERS
VOICE
am
The New-York Papers

NEW YORK
I ♥ NY
EVORK NEW YORK NEWY
NEW YORK NEW YORK N
EORK NEW YORK NEW
NEW YORK NEW YORK
ORK NEW YORK NEWY
I ♥ NY
RADIO CITY
New
NYPD
Mets
I ♥ NY
SOUVENIR OF YANKEE
Yankees
New York
NEW YORK
NYC
TAXI
New York
I ♥ NY
I ♥ NY
I ♥ NY
I ♥ NY
#1
Yankees
NY
NEW YORK . U.S.A
I ♥ NY.
NEW YORK
NEW YORK
I ♥ NY
THE EMPIRE STATE

Welcome to

Central Park

For further information on the Park please contact:

Park Office 638 56081

Carder/Ranger 69- 1458

Community Patrol 666 5865

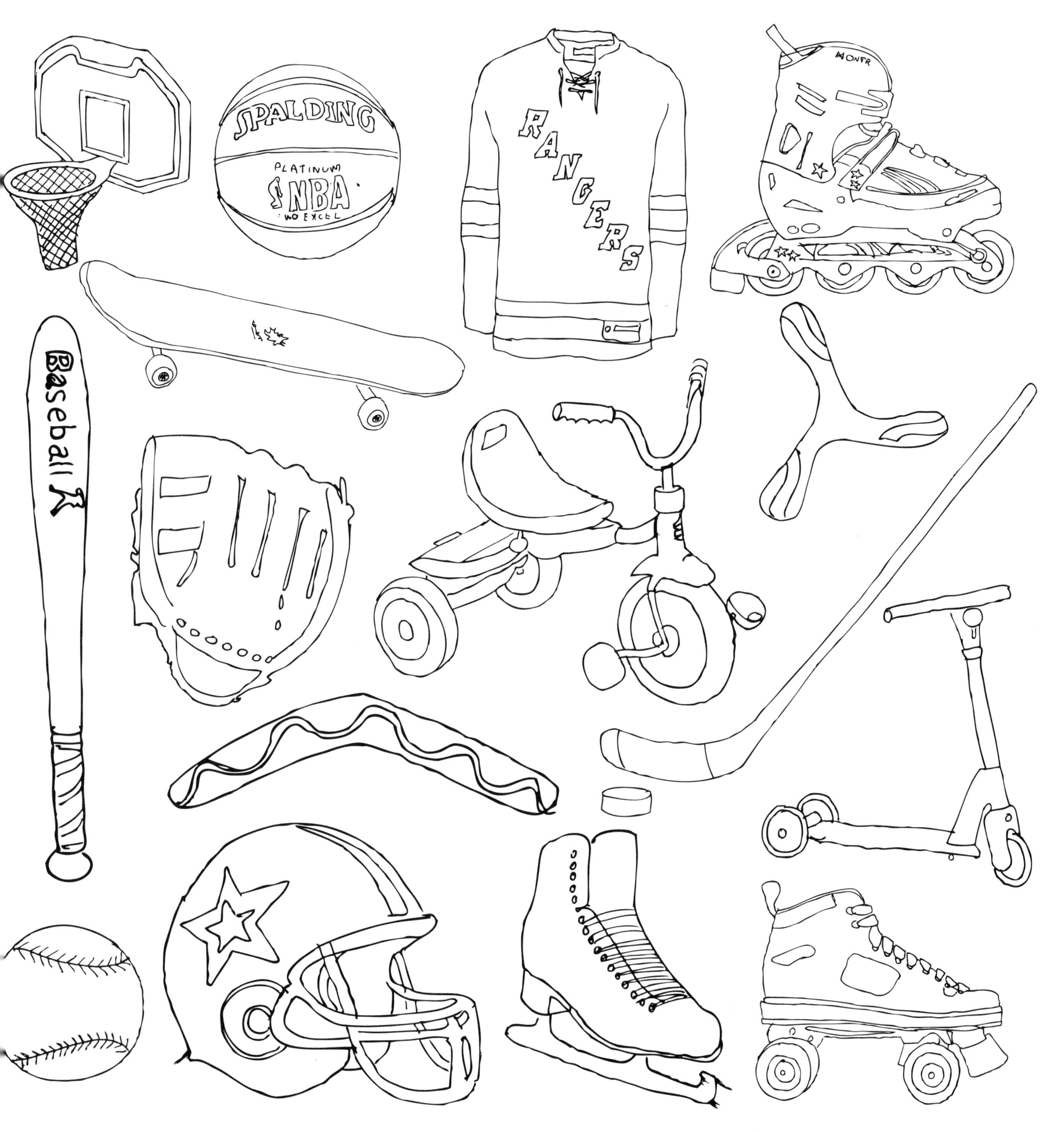
SPALDING
PLATINUM
NBA
RANGERS
Baseball

We are the 99%
AND
10 S LOVE ING ST

BIKE
like a
NEW
YORKER.

DEL MONICA'S
DEL MONICA'S

FRESH FRAGRANCE
AQUA NET
3
NARS
SEPHORA
NARS
LILY LOLO
benecos
PARURE DE LUMIÈRE
French Manicure
ciaté

100% Raw
ORGANIC
FOOD BAR
BIO
ACTIVE GREENS

VERY
BUSY
Day
Tan-tasche-tic
MILK
NO
SUGAR
KEEP
CALM
AND
CARRY
ON
stash
premium
tea

NEW YORK, I LOVE YOU.

COSMETICS
PRESCRIPTIONS
200

INTE
LLIG
ENT
SIA
THE SKY LINE FOODTRUCK

AMERICAN BEAR
AMERICAN OWNED
AMERICAN BREWED
PITTSBURGH BREWING COMPANY
HEENZ
CHILI SAUCE
HEENZ
YELLOW MUSTARD
Whole Grain
Cherrios
Made with wholegrain roots
Oat fibre helps lower cholesterol
260g
ORGANIC
Arrowheed Mills
Creamy Organic Peanut Butter
STARBUCKS COFFEE
HEENZ 57
HEENZ
TOMATO KETCHUP
KRAFT
macaroni & cheese
smm mile, the cheesiest
original flavor
Original Fruit
Skittles
WRIGLEY'S
Beg Red
BARBECUE SAUCE
HICKORY
HICKORY
OPEN HIT
AMERICAN
STOCQYERD
BBQ SAUCE
Since 1942
vlasic
Kosher Dill Spears
CLASSIC DILL TASTE
NEW!
CAP'N CRUNSH treats
peanut butter
MasterFoo
Mild America
MUSTAR
Pastrami CHALLANGE
POOND THE POONDER
2 FEET LONG & OVER 1 POUND OF PASTRAMI!
DOMINON
BACH HOUR
Golden Planer
DOMINON
OAK BARREL STOUT
PORDHOM
VISTERIA WHEAT

DANCE
Hello
"SHE IS TOO FOND OF COOKS, & IT HAS TURNED HER BRAIN."
The Monde of MarieLou
JOY
big fish
"I DON'T LIKE BAGS
except this one...
MOTHER OF THE WORLD

280

TAXI
NO.63
NYC

STUSY
fresh
POP CORN
DELICIOUS
CRISP
fresh
POP CORN
DELICIOUS
NUTRITIOUS
fresh
POP CORN
DELICIOUS
NUTRITIOUS
fresh
POP CORN
DELICIOUS
CRISP
STARBUCKS
COFFEE
BEN&JERRY'S
Schweddy
Balls
Thank you
Thank you

The Real American Hot Dog
HOT DOG 2$,50
MAXI HOT DOG 3$,90
1,50
3,50
4,90
AMERICAN'S HOT DOG
100% Beef
- Fat
+ taste

Phone
skype

Greenwich Village UNION SQUARE

New York Public Library

Statue of Liberty

5TH AVENUE Central Park

Metropolitan Museum of Art

NEW YORK

Empire State Grand Central

Building Terminal

MADISON ST. PAUL'S

CHAPEL

All STARS
ZX 730

BABBA

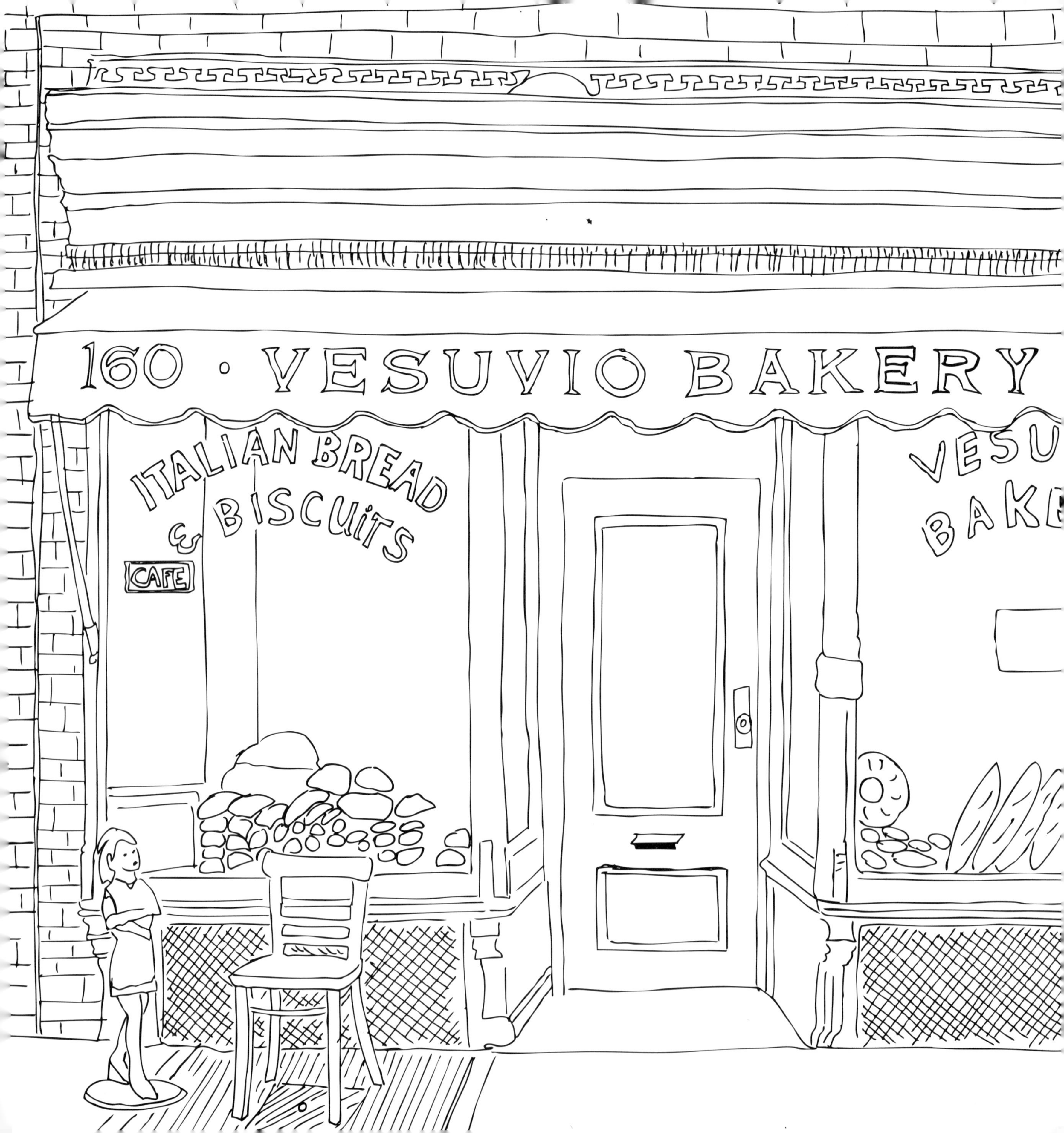

160 · VESUVIO BAKERY

ITALIAN BREAD & BISCUITS

CAFE

Sorry
WE'RE
CLOSED

ARGAN Oil
ORGANIC TOFU
NATURAL

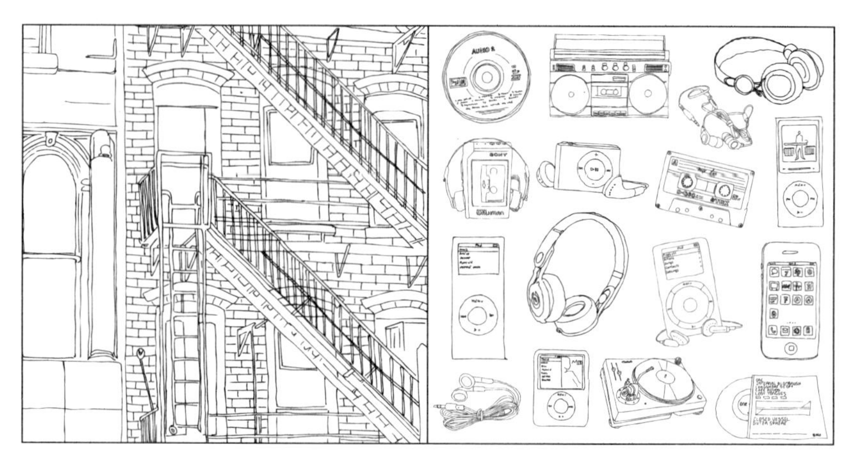

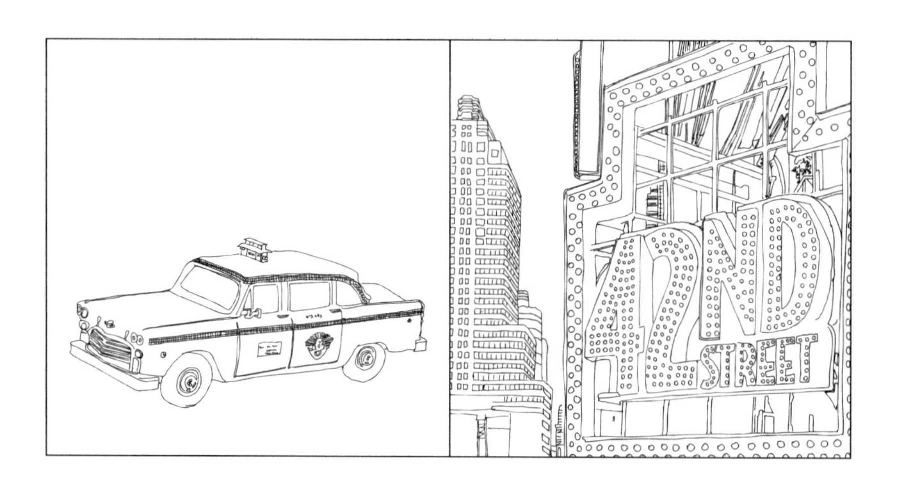
42ND STREET

Public
FISH MARKET
ICE CREAM
Public
FISH MARKET

CHELSEA
FLOWER
MARKET

PALACE
WEST SIDE STORY
BROADWAY'S SURE THING
CHICAGO
SOUTH PACIFIC

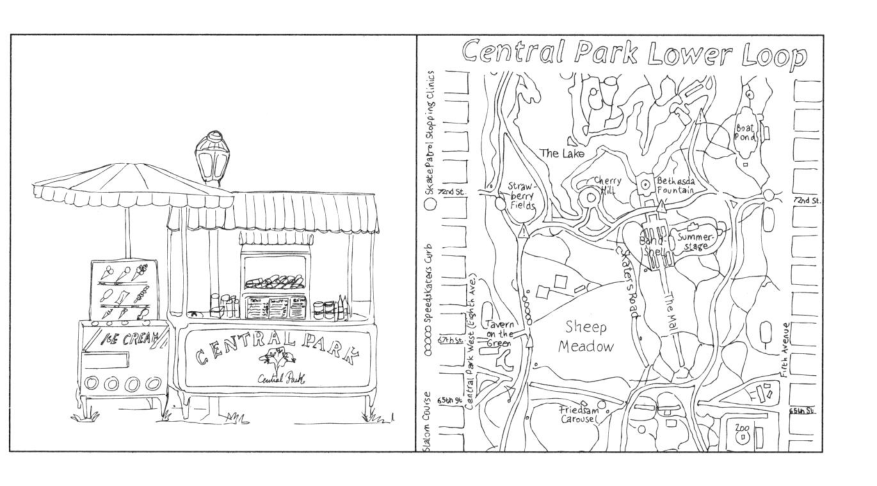
CENTRAL PARK
Central Park Lower Loop
The Lake
Strawberry Fields
Cherry Hill
Bethesda Fountain
Boat Pond
Summerstage
Sheep Meadow
Tavern on the Green
The Mall
Zoo
72nd St.

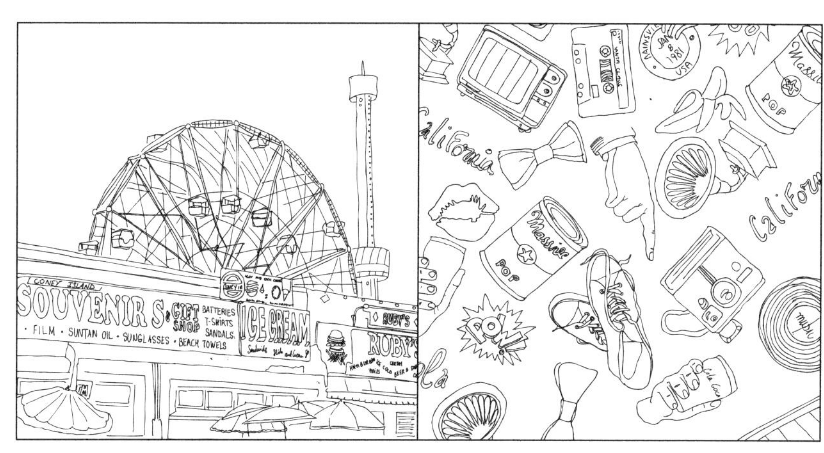
CONEY ISLAND
SOUVENIRS
GIFT SHOP
BATTERIES
T-SHIRTS
SANDALS
ICE CREAM
FILM · SUNTAN OIL · SUNGLASSES · BEACH TOWELS
RUBY'S
California
POP

Modern
SNACK BAR
SAUERBRATEN
SS CRABS
BEER & WINE
COCKTAILS

LI & SONS
285

NEW YORK
New York
NEW YORK
NEW YORK

Welcome to
Central Park
For further information on the Park please contact:
Park Office 638 56081
Carder/Ranger 69- 1459
Community Patrol 666 5865

BIKE
like a
NEW
YORKER.

AQUA NET

MILK
NO
SUGAR
KEEP
CALM
AND
CARRY
ON

NEW YORK,
I LOVE YOU.
COSMETICS
PRESCRIPTIONS
200

INTE
LLIG
ENT
SIA
Cheerios
Skittles
CHILI SAUCE
TOMATO KETCHUP

DANCE
Hello
JOY
MOTHER
WORLD
280

TAXI
NO. 63
NYC

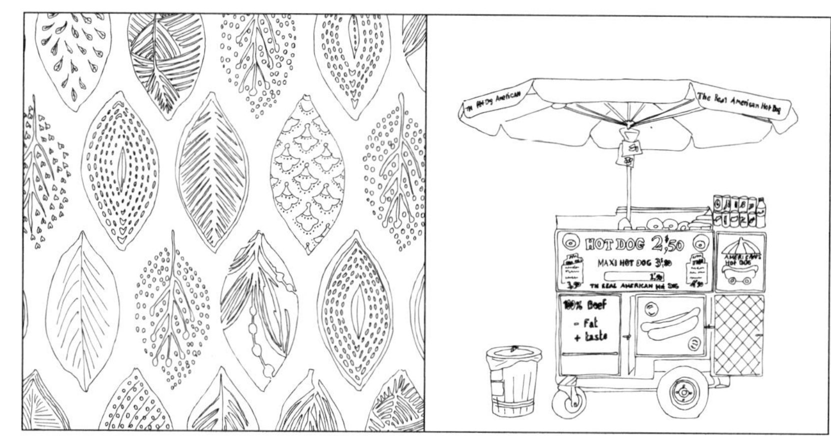
The Real American Hot Dog
HOT DOG

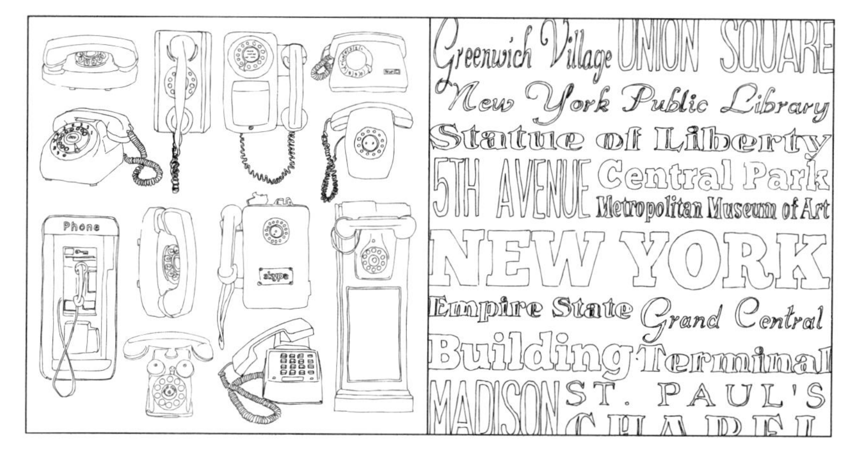
Phone
Greenwich Village
UNION SQUARE
New York Public Library
Statue of Liberty
5TH AVENUE
Central Park
Metropolitan Museum of Art
NEW YORK
Empire State Building
Grand Central Terminal
MADISON
ST. PAUL'S

160 · VESUVIO BAKERY
ITALIAN BREAD
& BISCUITS
Sorry
WE'RE
CLOSED